Penguin Education

**The Musical Instrument
Recipe Book**

# The
# Musical Instrument
# Recipe Book

Penguin Education

This edition is based on a book prepared with the support of National Science Foundation Grant Number G–21815. The views expressed herein are those of the authors, however, and do not necessarily represent those of the National Science Foundation.

Penguin Education
A Division of Penguin Books Ltd,
Harmondsworth, Middlesex, England
Penguin Books Australia Ltd,
Ringwood, Victoria, Australia

First published in the USA by Webster Division, McGraw-Hill Book Company, 1968
First published in Great Britain by Penguin Education, 1974
Copyright © Education Development Center Inc., 1968, 1971

Made and printed in Great Britain by
Richard Clay and Co. Ltd, Bungay, Suffolk
Set in IBM Univers by Herts Typesetting Services Limited, Hertford

# Contents

# Preface

The Elementary Science Study is one of many curriculum-development programmes in the fields of science, social studies and mathematics under preparation at Education Development Center, Inc. EDC (a private nonprofit organization, incorporating the Institute for Educational Innovation and Educational Services Incorporated) began in 1958 to develop new ideas and methods for improving the content and process of education in the USA.

ESS has been supported primarily by grants from the National Science Foundation. Development of materials for teaching science from kindergarten through eighth grade started on a small scale in 1960. The work of the project has since involved more than a hundred educators in the conception and design of its units of study. Among the staff have been scientists, engineers, mathematicians and teachers experienced in working with students of all ages, from kindergarten through college.

Equipment, films and printed materials are produced with the help of staff specialists, as well as of the film and photography studios, the design laboratory and the production shops of EDC. At every stage of development, ideas and materials are taken into actual classrooms, where children help shape the form and content of each unit before it is released to schools everywhere.

The **Musical Instrument Recipe Book** grew out of two instrument-making projects. During the early development of **Whistles and Strings,** Dan Watt and I were looking for ways to produce interesting sounds and make instruments from simple objects. At the same time, a few teachers in a summer workshop at the EDC Design Lab. in 1967 concentrated on making simple instruments for their classrooms. We eventually collected the best designs from both projects to make the Trial Teaching Edition of the **Musical Instrument Recipe Book.** Two teachers, Patricia A. Miller of Boston, Massachusetts, and Margery Thurber of Sudbury, Massachusetts, worked very closely with us on many of the early designs. Many of the instruments have been used with delight by the children in their classrooms. We have enjoyed and appreciated all the visits, letters, tapes and photographs we have received from instrument-making enthusiasts.

So many people have contributed suggestions, ideas and assistance for this edition that it is impossible to acknowledge each of them personally. I am indebted to George Cope, Joan Hamblin, David Alexander, Dan Watt and Lois Cannon for the photographs which appear in this book, to Gerald Foster and David Alexander for the drawings, to Adeline Naiman who edited the manuscript and to Nancy Weston who designed the book.

I should also like to thank Nat Burwash and Bruno Kansanniva of the EDC Design Lab, whose original designs for instruments, solutions to all sorts of design problems and continued enthusiasm for instrument building have made possible many improvements in the **Recipe Book.**

Emily Romney

# Introduction

Many children and adults like to build musical instruments. Anyone who makes even the simplest instrument becomes involved in working with tools and with the materials which he must alter and combine to build his design, and he listens critically to the sounds his instrument makes. There is great satisfaction in being able to make an instrument which is pleasing and which works.

The instruments in the **Recipe Book** can be constructed with simple tools and inexpensive, commonly available materials. Most of them are quite sturdy. The designs are simple and a number of them can be built in both simple and more complicated versions.

**Using the** Recipe Book

For each basic instrument, there are instructions given in a

8

cookery book format. Each 'recipe' tries to supply enough information to ensure success for a beginner. You'll also find photographs and drawings of variations on several of the basic designs, along with suggestions for alternative materials.

How carefully people need to follow the instructions will depend upon what they want to do. If someone is setting out to construct an exact copy of an instrument in the book, it is best to follow the recipe quite closely. Otherwise, there's no particular reason to stick to the instructions. Just browsing through the book has given many instrument builders ideas for inventing instruments or making their own version of ones that were already familiar.

In planning an instrument-making project, you'll need to gather tools and materials and to consider the kind of working space at your disposal. Also you should keep in mind how much experience you have had building things in and out of school.

**Some instruments are easier to construct than others.**

**1** These instruments can be made very easily.

ear harp

one-string stick guitar

bleach-bottle banjo

wind chimes

water bells

flowerpot bells (untuned)

wooden chimes (untuned)

sand blocks

wood-block tambourine

rhythm sticks

tongue-depressor finger piano (G-clamp version)

rattles

telephones

panpipe (untuned)

**2** These instruments require a few precise procedures. They can probably be made without much help from a teacher or an adult.

variations on the washtub bass

tuned flowerpot bells

hose horn

tuned panpipe

wood block

wooden drum

**3** These instruments require some skill with tools and a fair amount of care and precision. They are, however, among the most versatile and appealing.

metal chimes

garden-hose recorder

slide whistle

tuned wooden chimes

## Original Designs and Inventions

A good collection of interesting materials almost invariably inspires new ideas for instruments. As you gather supplies — besides materials for specific designs — bring in any oddments which look promising.

Certain materials seem to be especially versatile for instrument making. With fishing line, wooden boards of various sizes and screw eyes, children have made many different kinds of stringed instruments. They have used everything — from pocket combs and pencils to blocks of wood and paper cups – to make bridges for their string instruments. They have found that paper cups, wastepaper baskets, desk drawers and desk tops can make excellent resonators.

Hardboard is a cheap, resonant and easily-worked material which can be made into many varieties of string and rhythm instruments.

Plastic tubes are very good devices for exploring sounds made by columns of air. You can cut tubes of different lengths to play tunes, make wind instruments with holes and slides for pitch changes and combine plastic tubes of different diameters to make musically unpredictable contraptions.

Drums can be made from almost any kind of hollow container. Pieces of wood will vary in pitch and quality, depending on their variety, size and shape. Odd pieces of metal, from washers to knives and forks, make interesting sounds when struck, as do different kinds of bottles, cups and glasses.

Informal exploration of sounds can often lead to an idea for an original instrument. That's how many of the instruments in the **Recipe Book** came about.

## Materials

Besides buying materials, you may find a good many items at home or at school. Some shopkeepers and merchants in your area may be willing to give you small quantities of materials. You may also have good luck in obtaining such things as scrap wood at timberyards, empty plastic bottles at laundries and tubing from discarded fixtures at plumbing suppliers, junk yards or the town dump.

Each recipe in this book gives a list of the materials you will need to make that particular design. On pages 16—18 is a general list of all the materials that are used to make the instruments in this book and suggestions for places to find them.

## Tools

You may be able to find all the tools you need at home or around the school. Each recipe gives a list of the tools you will need to make that design.

All these tools can be purchased at ironmongers:

hammer

handsaw (a 10-point crosscut saw with a 20 in blade is a good kind to buy)

hacksaw (a junior hacksaw with 6 in blades is best)

keyhole saw or fretsaw

tube cutter (the Record tube cutter, no. 200-3, costs £1.25 and is available from most large tool shops)

sandpaper, emery paper

ruler

single-edge razor blade

pliers

stanley knife or other utility knife

6 in hacksaw blade

drill (hand or electric) and ¼ in bit for drill vice or metre block

You will need a vice or some kind of bracing device to hold metal and wood in place while you saw or cut. Carpentry or classroom workbenches usually come with a vice attached. No inexpensive clamp-on vice tried has worked well enough to be recommended, but the home-made mitre blocks described below are good substitutes for a vice and are fairly simple to make.

With one of these, you can saw or drill on any ordinary desk or work top without damage.

To make the mitre block in this picture, nail **and** glue pieces of wood of the following sizes together:

One 12 in length of 1 in by 8 in (bottom)

One 3 in length of 1 in by 8 in (brace to overlap table)

One 3 in length of 1 in by 6 in (crossbar)

Two 6 in lengths of 2 in by 3 in (guides)

Be sure to leave a space between the two guides for the saw.

In the picture is another sturdy mitre block made from scrap wood, glue and nails. The mitre block can be used for sawing, drilling and for cutting metal tubes.

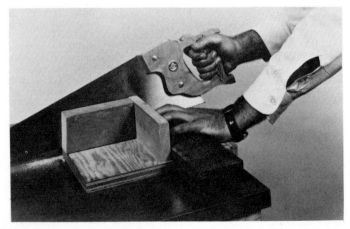

The saw is guided by the slot.

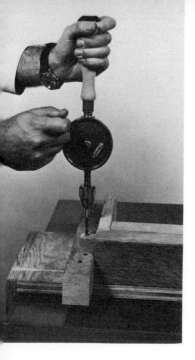

The mitre block keeps the wood from spinning while it is being drilled. You will find it easier if someone else holds the wood against the mitre block while you drill.

This takes two people — one person to turn the tube cutter and another to hold the tube steady.

| Materials | Available from |
|---|---|
| cord (thin clothes line will do) | home or school |
| glasses, jars, bottles | |
| scraps of metal or glass | |
| scraps of plastic sponge | |
| crown bottle tops | |
| small containers for rattles | |
| small objects to fill rattles (beans, tacks, pebbles) | |
| broomsticks | |
| drawing pins | |
| paper or plastic cups, yoghurt pots | |
| paper clips | |
| vacuum-cleaner or hair-dryer hose | |
| large metal containers (washtubs, buckets, wastepaper baskets, oil or paint tins) | |
| large plastic bottles (bleach or orange-juice bottles or other large plastic containers) | |
| plastic and metal funnels | |
| ice-lolly sticks | |
| postal tubes | stationers |
| masking tape | |
| large and small nails | Woolworths or any ironmongers |
| ¼ in screw eyes | |
| Evo-stik resin W or an equivalent wood glue | |
| sisal twine | |
| medium-sized G-clamps (4 in is a good size) | |

| | |
|---|---|
| plastic garden hose<br>gardening twine<br>earthenware flowerpots<br>bamboo poles | gardening shops |
| hardboard<br>aluminium angle (½ in by ¹⁄₁₆ in)<br>long dowels of various sizes | do-it-yourself shops or<br>builders merchants |
| central-heating piping<br>stiff plastic tubing of various<br>  diameters | plumbers or central-heating<br>suppliers |
| scraps of wood in various sizes<br>  and shapes | timberyards or builders<br>merchants |
| electrical conduit piping<br>  (this may be difficult to find,<br>  but it's worth trying) | electrical shops |
| tongue depressors or wooden<br>  spatulas | Boots or other large chemists |
| Insta-heat | educational suppliers<br>(catering department) or by<br>post from The Insta-heat<br>Company, 91 Shaftesbury<br>Avenue, London W1V 8AJ<br>(10p for 2⅝ oz or 20p<br>for a 7 oz tin) |
| monofilament nylon fishing line<br>  (sea-line with a breaking<br>  strength of 36 lb is a good<br>  sort) | fishing tackle shops |

There are a lot of things which you may be able to get for
nothing by asking politely.

| | |
|---|---|
| wooden boxes | off-licenses or wine merchants |
| off-cuts of wood | timberyards |
| off-cuts of piping | plumbers |
| large cardboard tubes | drapers or anywhere where they sell fabric by the yard |
| large tins and plastic containers | the school kitchen |

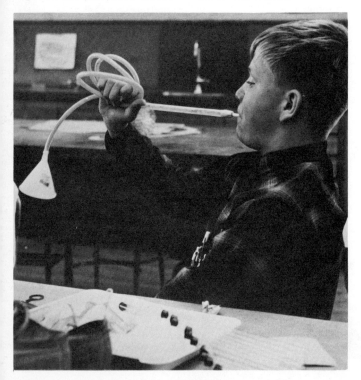

# Book List

| Title | Author | Publisher |
|-------|--------|-----------|
| Musical Instruments Made to be Played | Ronald Roberts | Dryad |
| Make Your Own Musical Instruments (available from The Project Club Milk Marketing Board) | Anna Deverson | Wolfe Publishing |
| Make Your Own Musical Instruments | Muriel Mendell and Robert Wood | Sterling Publishing |
| The Meaning and Magic of Music | Peter Gammond | Hamlyn |
| Drums, Rattles and Bells | Larry Kettelkamp | Wheaton of Exeter |
| Musical Instruments Through the Ages | Anthony Baines | Faber |
| Musical Instruments | Karl Geiringer | Allen & Unwin |
| What is Sound | Reuben Gabriel | Collins |
| Musical Instruments in Art and History | Roger Bragard and Ferdinand De Hen | The Cresset Press |
| Crafts for All | Karl Hills | Routledge & Kegan Paul |
| Musical Instruments from the Renaissance to the 19th Century | Sergio Paganelli | Hamlyn |
| The Instruments of Music | Robert Donington | University Paperbacks (Methuen) |
| Sound Sense | Geoffrey Russell-Smith | Boosey & Hawkes |

**Musical Instruments**

**Making Musical Instruments and Apparatus for Use in Nursery and Infant Schools**

Jean Jenkins

Kathleen Blocksidge

GLC

Nursery Schools Association

# Ear Harp

**Materials**

15 in length of plank (pine or other soft wood) about ⅞ in by 12 in (sold as 1 in by 12 in at timberyards). If possible, get 'select' pine which has no knots in it

monofilament nylon fishing line. A good sort to use is sea-line with a breaking strength of 36 lb. It is interesting to experiment with different sorts of line. The greater the breaking strength the lower the pitch of the note will be

6 or 8 nails about 1½ in long with heads

either 6 or 8 screw eyes (¼ in) and a large nail or 1½ ft of ¼ in dowel and masking tape for tuning pegs

## Tools

hammer

ruler

saw

drill (hand or electric) ⎤
                        ⎬ for tuning pegs
¼ in bit                ⎦

sandpaper

Draw a line near and parallel to one edge of the board.

Then draw a slanting line from an opposite corner.

Hammer an evenly spaced row of nails partway into the board along one of the lines, one nail for each string.

## Two ways to finish your ear harp

**1 Screw eyes.** Using the large nail to start the hole, insert a screw eye partway into the board along the other line opposite the first nail.

Then attach a piece of fishing line to the nail with a good, firm knot. Pull the string fairly tight and tie it securely to the screw eye. You can make the strings tighter by turning the screw eyes.

Do the same for the other strings.

Screw eyes are easier to turn if you use a nail through the eye as a lever.

After the rest of the strings are connected, tune them as you like by tightening or loosening them.

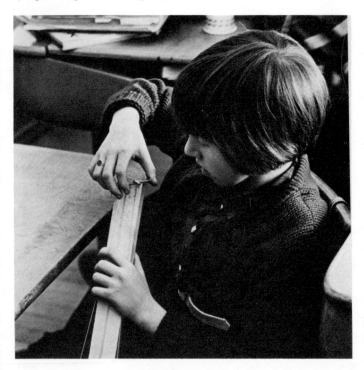

**2 Tuning pegs.** These can be used for other string instruments as well. Instruments with tuning pegs seem to have a richer sound than those with screw eyes. Screw eyes are easier to insert but pegs can be twisted farther for tuning and they look nicer!

To make tuning pegs, you need

¼ in diameter doweling (2 in piece for each peg)

drill (hand or electric)

¼ in bit for drill

sandpaper

saw

masking tape

Saw the doweling into 2 in pegs. (Make one for each string.) Sand each peg on one end so that the last ½ inch is flat on one side. Then flatten the other side on the same end. (Wrapping the sandpaper around a ruler makes it easier to sand flat.)

Drill a ¼ inch hole through your board for each peg. Attach one of the strings to a nail on the other end of the board with a good firm knot. Then put about 3 inches of masking tape along the free end of the string — sticky side towards the string. Wind the taped part of the string around the peg just below the flat end. Force the round end of the peg into its hole until it is firmly in place. You can tighten or loosen the string by turning the pegs. A wooden clothes peg fitted over the flat end of a peg makes it easy to turn the peg for tuning.

## How does it sound?

If you hold the back of the harp against your ear while you play it, the sound will seem richer and warmer to you. Also some ear harps sound stronger if you prop them up on a table with a block of wood under one corner. If you want your harp to sound **much** louder, hook up a microphone to the loudspeaker system of a tape recorder or a record player and put the microphone on the board while you pluck the strings. Try this with other instruments, too.

# One-String Stick Guitar

Here is a one-string version of the ear harp. You can play different notes by pressing the string against the wood in different places while you pluck it.

## Materials

1 24 in length of wood about ⅞ in by 1⅞ in (sold as 1 in by 2 in at timberyards)

1 yd monofilament nylon fishing line

2 ice-lolly sticks

**either** two screw eyes (¼ in) and a large nail **or** a large nail and a 2 in length of ¼ in dowel and masking tape for a tuning peg

## Tools

saw

hammer

drill (hand or electric)  } for tuning peg
¼ in bit for drill

Insert a screw eye near each end of the wood strip, or substitute a large nail at one end and a tuning peg at the other. The kind of peg described on page 25 will work well.

Saw a shallow groove across the strip about 1½ inches from each end.

Insert the ice-lolly sticks sideways into the grooves, and tie the string between the two screw eyes or the nail and the peg.

Using the large nail as a lever, tighten the string by turning one of the screw eyes or use a clothespeg to turn the peg.

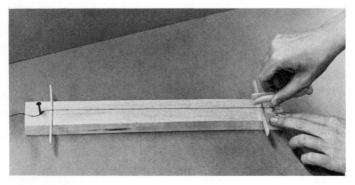

The one-string stick guitar will sound louder if it rests on top of a wooden table or a large hollow container, and it will also sound much louder to you if you hold the back of the strip against your ear while you play.

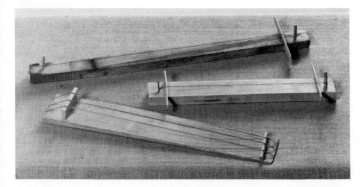

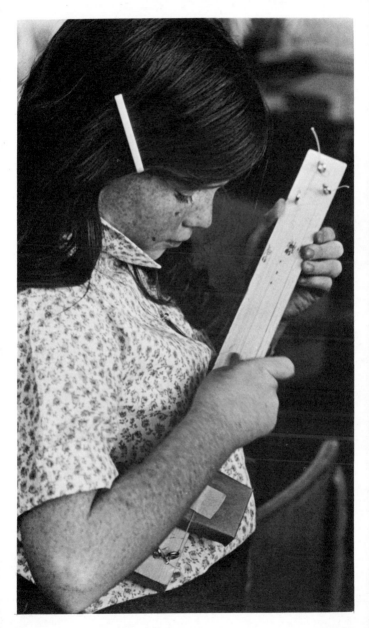

# Bleach-Bottle Banjo

## Materials

1 plastic bleach bottle or other large plastic bottle[1]

30 in length of wood, 2 in by ⅞ in or 3 in by ⅞ in (sold as 1 in by 2 in or 1 in by 3 in at timberyards)

about 3 yd of monofilament nylon fishing line

a cork or a small piece of wood (about ¾ in by 2 in by ¼ in) and a screw eye

**either** 6 or 8 screw eyes and a large nail **or** about 6 in of ¼ in diameter doweling and masking tape for pegs

## Tools

saw

hammer

utility knife

drill (hand or electric) ⎱
¼ in bit for drill ⎰ for tuning pegs

[1] Try any other hollow containers, such as one end of a large cardboard postal tube. Big cardboard tubes can often be got from drapers or other shops where they sell fabric.

Cut an H-shaped slot the size of the large wood strip starting about 1 inch from the bottom of the plastic bleach bottle. The wood strip should fit tightly into the slot when the sides of the H are folded out.

Make an identical slot in the same spot on the opposite side of the bottle.

Using the large nail to start the holes, insert a screw eye (or a nail) for each string you want near one end of the wood strip. Space the screw eyes evenly. Then slide the strip through the bleach bottle, with the nails or screw eyes turned toward·the bottom of the bottle.

Insert the same number of screw eyes or tuning pegs in the other end of the strip. (See page 25 for making tuning pegs.) Then tie fishing line tightly between each pair of screw eyes or between the nails and pegs.

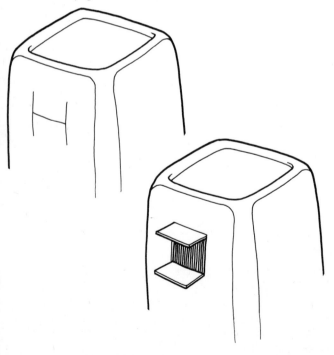

## To make a bridge

Here are two ways to make a bridge:

**1** Slide a piece of cork or a small piece of wood propped up with a screw eye between the bleach bottle and the strings (see pictures).

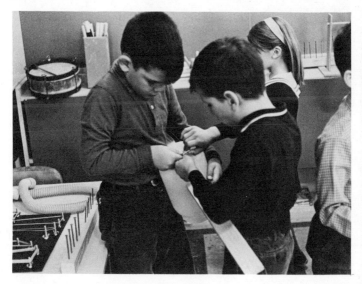

**2** Insert a screw eye into the centre of a small piece of wood, so that the wood will stand in a slanting position. You may have to make a small notch for each string in the top of the bridge to keep the strings from sliding off.

To tune the strings, tighten or loosen them by turning the screw eyes or pegs on the wood strip. (Use the large nail as a lever to turn the screws or a wooden clothes peg or pliers for the pegs.)

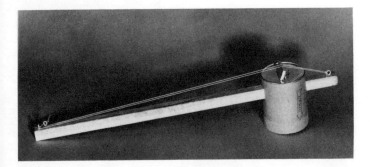

# Variations on the Washtub Bass

The washtub bass is a delightful instrument. The classic version employs a washtub for the sound box — hence the name — but other varieties can be made in many sizes out of different materials. All you need is a stick, a string and a hollow container as a resonator.

Here is one which is inexpensive and easy to make.

## Materials

1 hollow container — gallon paint tin, wastepaper basket, cardboard bucket, etc.

30 in dowel or other stick, ¾ in or more in diameter

3 ft to 4 ft piece of string (sisal or gardening twine is a good kind)

wooden peg or small piece of dowel (1 in to 2 in long)

## Tools

saw

hammer

drill (hand or electric)

¼ in bit for drill

## To attach the stick and string

Drill a hole through one end of the stick, about 1 inch from the end. In the other end of the stick saw a ⅛ inch groove perpendicular to the direction of the hole. (This groove will hold the lower edge of the stick in position on the rim of the bucket.)

Then tie a small wooden peg or dowel securely to one end of the string. Punch a hole in the centre of the bottom of the bucket. Thread the string through the hole in the bucket from the inside to the outside. (The peg will act as a brace against the hole.)

Thread the free end of the string through the hole in the stick, and tie a large knot to hold it securely.

## Getting ready to play

Hook the notched end of the stick over the rim of the bucket. Brace the bucket by putting one foot on the opposite rim. Pull the stick towards you with one hand to tighten the string, and pluck away with the other!

The pitch of the sound will change when you tighten or loosen the tension on the string by moving the stick back and forth. The pitch also changes when you press the string against the stick with your fingers at different places. The bass will sound more resonant if there is a small hole in the side of the cardboard bucket.

## A larger version

For a larger version of the washtub bass (producing lower notes), these materials work well:

broomstick or other stick of comparable size

metal washtub, metal wastepaper basket, 2-gallon oil can, any large tin can or a wooden tea-chest

heavy string (nylon cord or thin clothesline is fine, and sisal or gardening twine is excellent)

The bass will sound more resonant if there is a piece of wood under one edge of the metal tub.

If pressing the string down on the large bass is too hard on your hand, hold a piece of cardboard between your hand and the string as you play.

# Water Bells

Water bells are easy to make. You'll need a supply of water and some drinking glasses or other glass containers that respond with clear ringing sounds when you strike them. Wooden pencils or dowels make good strikers.

Adding water to the containers will change the pitch of the sounds. To get a good range of pitches, you will probably need

more than one size of container, since the difference in pitch between a full container and an empty one of the same size is often no more than a few notes.

Water bells are excellent instruments to use for experimenting with pitch changes, and for playing tunes and making up songs, too.

# Wind Chimes

Wind chimes can be made from many materials:

various kinds of nails

scraps of metal

pieces of glass or plastic (coloured glass is beautiful moving in the sunshine)

strips of wood

dowels

pieces of bamboo

short pieces of aluminium tubing[1] and aluminium angle (both ¼ in diameter tubing and ½ in diameter angle make a strong, clear ringing sound)

Hang the pieces of material you choose, so that they will strike one another when they move.

[1] For a tuned set of chimes from thin aluminium tubing, see page 46.

Suspend them from a straight bar or, for more collisions, hang them from a small triangular frame made by nailing three pieces of wood together. They may also be suspended from a circular band made from metal stripping, a small cheese box lid or an embroidery hoop or from any small piece of pegboard, heavy cardboard or metal sheeting.

For a variety of sounds, use pieces of several different sizes (the exact dimensions aren't important).

These chimes are made of aluminium angle.

# Flowerpot Bells

**Materials**

flowerpots

cord

a few ice-lolly sticks or wood scraps

a pencil or dowel for a striker

Clean, unglazed, earthenware flowerpots make beautiful bells.
A number of different-sized pots hung on a cord from a support
will give you a range of tones.

If you want a set of bells to play the scale or other pattern, you
will need to compare the sounds of several pots to find a group in
tune with one another. (Flowerpots of the same size often differ
in pitch by as much as one or two scale tones.)

**Be sure to test the flowerpots before you buy them**

In a tuned set, duplicates of some of the pots and a few very low tones come in handy for group song playing and for making harmonies.

## Flowerpots are fragile

Even the slightest crack may spoil the tone, so be careful about hitting the pots too hard.

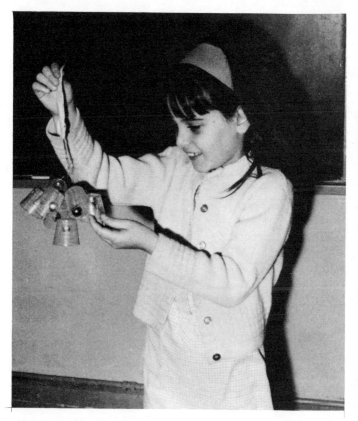

These 'jingle bells' are made from plastic cups with small bells attached to wires for clappers.

# Metal Chimes

Chimes made from electrical conduit tubing have beautiful tone quality and are inexpensive to make. If you cannot get hold of electrical conduit tubing, use central-heating tubing instead. Plumbers and central-heating installers will often give you off-cuts for nothing.

**Materials**

2 10 ft pieces of ½ in diameter electrical conduit tubing

string

masking tape

**Tools**

hacksaw or tube cutter[1]

vice or benchhook for holding the tubing while you cut it (see pages 13–15).

[1] Hacksaws are often more readily available, but a good-quality tube cutter is much easier to use and to control. One kind of tube cutter to purchase is suggested on page 12.

Cut one tube of each length shown in the drawing. Measure the tubing carefully before cutting.

Tie double knots in both ends of 8 inch pieces of string. Then attach the string to the top of each tube with a piece of masking tape.[2]

[2] If you have a metal drill, you can drill holes at one end of the tube to attach the string. It doesn't spoil the sound.

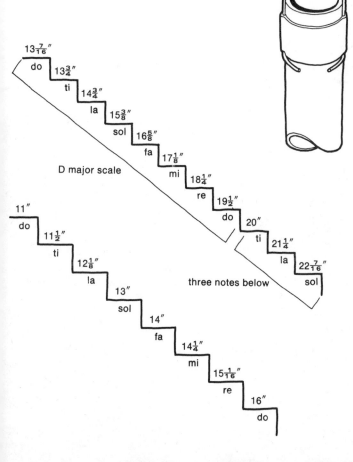

$13\frac{7}{16}''$
do

$13\frac{3}{4}''$
ti

$14\frac{3}{4}''$
la

$15\frac{3}{8}''$
sol

$16\frac{5}{8}''$
fa

$17\frac{1}{8}''$
mi

$18\frac{1}{4}''$
re

$19\frac{1}{2}''$
do

$20''$
ti

$21\frac{1}{4}''$
la

$22\frac{7}{16}''$
sol

D major scale

three notes below

$11''$
do

$11\frac{1}{2}''$
ti

$12\frac{1}{8}''$
la

$13''$
sol

$14''$
fa

$14\frac{1}{4}''$
mi

$15\frac{1}{16}''$
re

$16''$
do

## Tuning the chimes

It is only possible to make the pitch of a tube higher (by shortening it). If the pitch of a tube is too low, trim a little off one end. Test the sound. If the pitch is still too low, trim off a little more.

If the pitch is too high, you'll have to cut another, slightly longer piece.

Hang the chimes at a convenient playing height. A classroom map frame does nicely as a support, or you may want to make one especially for the chimes.

If you need hooks to attach the chimes to a support, shower curtain rings, S-shaped drapery hooks, or opened paper clips work well.

**Small tuned chimes**

You can make tuned or untuned chimes from narrow tubing or from aluminium angle. The method is about the same as for the larger chimes, except that you use narrower pieces of tape and monofilament fishing line to hang the chimes or drill holes in each tube and string them with the monofilament. (Don't use tape on aluminium angle. It spoils the tone.)

For a tuned set of chimes made from aluminium tubing with a ¼ inch outside diameter, cut one tube in each of the lengths shown in the drawing.

# Wooden Chimes

Bars of wood struck with a hard object and allowed to vibrate freely make sounds of definite pitch. As a rule, the longer the piece of wood, the lower the sound it makes. Any group of random lengths will give you a variety of sounds. (See below for ways to suspend the bars.) With a bit more effort, it is possible to make a tuned set. Here are directions for making a set with which you can play an A major scale.

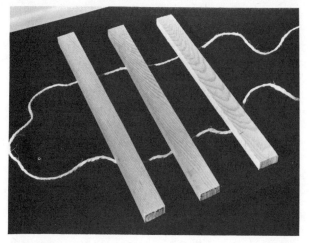

## Materials

12 ft length of wood, ⅞ in by ⅞ in (sold in timberyards as 1 in by 2 in) Soft woods, such as clear pine, are inexpensive and are easy to work with. **Avoid knotty pine. The knots almost invariably deaden the tone**

6 ft of heavy twine (sisal or gardening twine works well)

piece of doweling or other wooden stick for a striker

screw eyes or staples

## Tools

saw

stapler or hammer

Measure the wood carefully before you cut it into bars, one each of these lengths:

| | |
|---|---|
| 20 in | 16½ in |
| 19 in | 15½ in |
| 18 in | 14½ in |
| 17½ in | 13½ in |

## Tuning

The set of bars will need some fine adjustments to play a proper scale. Here are some suggestions. A convenient way to arrange the bars for comparing the sounds they make is to lay all of them out in order from shortest to longest on a piece of rope or twine. The vibration pattern in a wooden bar is such that there is a node point or 'dead spot' about one-quarter of the way in from each end of the bar. If you arrange the bars so that they touch the twine only at these two points, they will be able to vibrate freely and produce a clear tone. (If the twine or the table top or your fingers touch other places on a bar, the sound may be deadened.)

Start with the longest (20 inch) bar as the low **do,** and tune the other pieces in order. Tune the 19 inch piece so that the first two pieces play **do-re.** Then add the 18 inch piece and adjust it so that all three pieces sound out **do-re-mi.** Continue with each piece until the whole scale is in tune.

To make the sound higher, saw a small piece off the end of the strip.

To make the sound lower, saw into the strip this way.

**To make the sound of a bar a little higher,** saw a bit off one end.
**To make the sound lower,** saw a little way into the bar,
perpendicular to the length, in the middle of the bar. In both
cases, a little cutting can make a lot of difference in the sound, so
go easy.

### Some further notes on tuning

Tune in a quiet place.

**Take your time.** If you find it hard at first to hear pitch
relationships between the bars, keep playing them until their
sound is quite familiar to you. Most people's ability to hear pitch
differences improves dramatically after they work with an
instrument for a time.

If you can't manage the tuning alone, **ask someone to help you.**

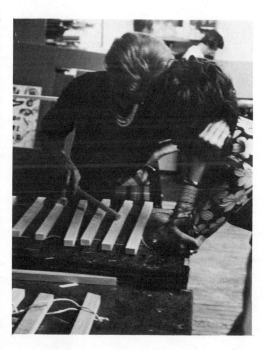

## Two ways to finish your instrument

**1** If you want your instrument to resemble a xylophone, complete it this way. Make a long, upside-down U-shape out of the piece of twine. Arrange the bars on top of the twine in order — shortest bar at the curve of the U and the longest bar nearest the open end of the U. Insert each bar between the strands of the twine by untwisting the twine just enough to push the bar ends through. The strands of twine should encircle the bars about one-quarter of the way in on each side (at the node points). When all the pieces are in place, the twine can be stapled to the bars of wood.

Tie a knot in the ends of the twine to prevent it from unravelling. The instrument can be laid flat on a table to be played, or it can be carried about or hung from a support and played in a vertical position. Wooden drumsticks, dowels or mallets (made by gluing a cotton reel onto the end of a stick) make good strikers.

**2** If you wish to hang the bars like chimes, insert a screw eye in the end of each bar and thread a length of string through the eye to make a loop. Suspend the bars from a broom handle, a wooden bar or a classroom map frame.

# Hose Horn

Here is an instrument that you can play like a bugle or use as a talking tube.

## Materials

piece of plastic or rubber garden hose (any length)

fairly large plastic or metal funnel

2 oz plastic funnel

masking tape

## Tools

pair of pliers, test-tube holders or tongs

stanley knife

heat source (tin of Insta-heat, Bunsen burner or gas stove)

The body of the horn is a piece of garden hose with a funnel inserted in the end. The connector on the end of the hose can be used as a mouthpiece for the horn. You can make a mouthpiece for a piece of hose with no connector from a 2 ounce plastic funnel like this:

Cut the funnel down with a stanley knife to about 1 inch length.[1]

Hold the cut edge of the funnel over a flame with pliers or tongs until the plastic softens. (If you hold the plastic over the flame for too long after it melts, it may begin to burn.)

[1] Cutting stiff plastic with a stanley knife can be dangerous. Younger children should have adults or children experienced with the tool do the cutting for them.

Let the plastic cool for about one minute, and then press the end straight down on a smooth surface to make a lip around the edge.

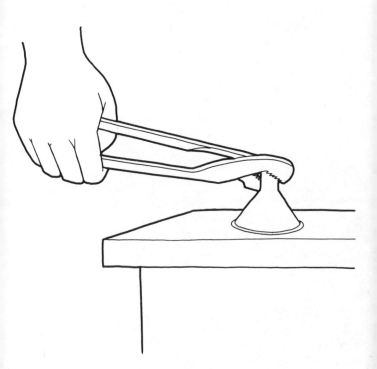

Insert the funnel into the end of the hose, and tape it in place with masking tape.

Press your lips together tightly and blow out hard through them to make a buzzing or 'razzing' sound. Blowing a horn in this way produces a resonant, bugle-like sound. The pitch of the sound depends on how tightly your lips are compressed and on how long the tube is.

Don't be discouraged if you don't get a good sound on the first try. You will get the knack of it with a little practice.

# Garden-Hose Recorder

**Materials**

piece of plastic garden hose, about 12 in long (transparent green hose with ⅛ in wall works well)

1 in piece of dowel, wide enough to fit **snugly** inside hose

**Tools**

stanley knife or other sharp knife

12 in piece of dowel, which fits **loosely** into hose

coarse sandpaper

## Cutting the air hole[1]

Cut an air hole like the one below, 1 inch from the end of the
piece of hose. (You may want to trace the pattern and mark it on
your hose.) It's much easier to cut the hose if you put the long
**loose-fitting** dowel into the hose for a brace.

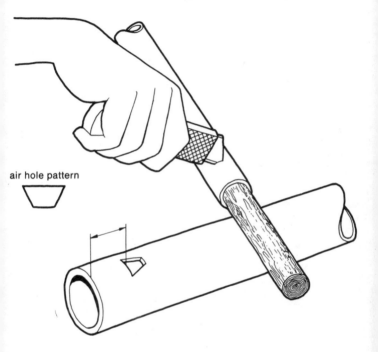

air hole pattern

## Making the mouthpiece plug

With the sandpaper flat on the table, sand the dowel until you
have a smooth, flat, slanting surface along one side.

[1] Cutting a neat hole in plastic with a stanley knife is difficult for young
children. Adults or older children experienced with the tool should do the
cutting for them.

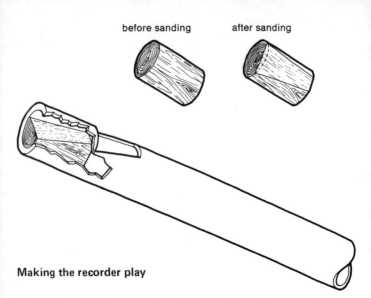

before sanding          after sanding

## Making the recorder play

When you have sanded the plug, put it into the end of the
recorder so that the sanded surface slants **up** to the air hole as
shown.

If you are very lucky, you will blow a clear note right away.

If the recorder doesn't play well at first, try moving the plug
backward or forward a little in the tube.

If it is hard to blow, the plug probably needs more sanding.

If there is a large air passage but the recorder still doesn't play,
you may need to make the slant of the plug steeper.

If you have sanded the plug too much, you may need to get
another piece of dowel and start again. However, don't start again
until you have tried everything else.

## More notes

When your recorder will play one note nicely, you may want to
make note holes.

First, just try blowing your recorder very softly, then harder and harder. See how many notes you can get simply by blowing in different ways.

Then insert the long, loose-fitting dowel into the hose again at the end opposite the mouthpiece.

With your stanley knife, make a ¼ inch square hole about 1½ inches from the end of the hose.

Play the recorder while you cover and uncover the hole. Then add as many holes as you like, keeping them about 1 inch apart. With each new hole, play the recorder to see how it sounds.

## A recorder tuned to the major scale

To make a recorder that will play a scale involves precise work.

Use a piece of hose exactly 12⅜ inches long with a ½ inch **inside** diameter. Make all the note holes ¼ inch square and place them as shown in the drawing.

Don't be discouraged if your first attempt isn't perfect. This is a hard instrument to make, and you may have to make more than one to get a recorder that will play in tune.

mouthpiece end

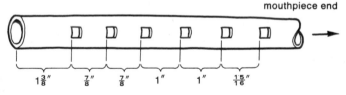

$1\frac{3}{8}''$    $\frac{7}{8}''$    $\frac{7}{8}''$    $1''$    $1''$    $1\frac{5}{16}''$

## Playing notes

To play the first note of the scale, cover all the holes and blow softly. For the next six notes, remove one finger at a time, starting from the lower end of the tube. To get the highest note of the scale, replace all your fingers on the holes, and blow a little harder than you did before.

## Variations

Any kind of fairly stiff tubing can be used to make a recorder.
Simply make sure that you have a dowel for the mouthpiece that
fits snugly into the tube. Use the pattern on page 61 as a model
for your air hole, making adjustments for differences in diameter
(wider hose, bigger air hole). It's best to make the air hole a little
bit on the small side and then enlarge it if necessary.

A length of hula hoop will make a simple flute. Cut a piece about
12 inches long, and make a shallow hole about 1 inch wide about
1 inch from one end. Plug the end near the hole with a cork or a
piece of dowel. Blow across the edge of the hole — as you would
blow on a pop bottle.

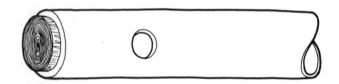

# Slide Whistle

## Materials

stiff plastic tubing, 12 in or longer

piece of dowel, 1 in long which fits snugly inside tube (for mouthpiece)

thinner piece of dowel, about 2 in to 3 in longer than tube (for slide)

small scrap of plastic household sponge, about ¼ in thick

Evo-stik resin W or equivalent

## Tools

stanley knife or scissors for cutting tubing

coarse sandpaper

piece of dowel, at least 4 in to 5 in long, to fit loosely inside tube

## Making the slide

Cut a circle out of sponge slightly larger than the diameter of your tube. Then glue the sponge circle to the end of the dowel to make a plunger. (Let the glued plunger stand for at least half an hour before you try to use the slide.) The sponge circle should fit tightly inside the tube. If it is too tight a fit to slide evenly, trim a little from the edges.

## Making the mouthpiece and the air hole

This is the same as for the garden-hose recorder (see pages 60–64).

## Making the whistle play

When you have sanded the plug so that it looks like the one in the diagram, insert it into the mouthpiece end of the tube. The flat surface should slant up to the air hole. When your whistle is finished, it should look like this:

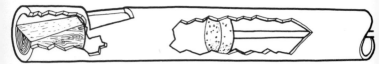

You can make different notes by blowing harder or softer, and by moving the slide in or out.

## A different kind of slide

You can make a very sturdy slide by using two pieces of dowel instead of one — a short piece which is almost as wide as the tube and a long, thinner piece.

Drill a hole in the centre of one end of the short piece, just big enough to hold the end of the thin dowel.

Glue the dowels together, and then glue the sponge circle onto the end of the thick dowel. (Allow time for the glue to dry.) Your slide will now look like this:

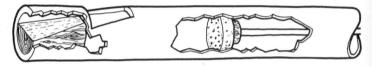

## 'Roll-your-own' variation

Make a 'roll-your-own' slide whistle, with a piece of fairly stiff (but still flexible) plastic sheeting, about 12 inches by 3 inches, and a 15 inch piece of dowel, ¾ inch to 1 inch in diameter.

Using this pattern, make an air hole an inch from one end of the plastic sheet.

air hole

Then simply roll the plastic sheet around the dowel to form a tube. Adjust the plastic until the dowel slides fairly easily in the tube. Tape the tube together with masking tape to fix the shape.

Cut a 1 inch piece from the dowel for the mouthpiece plug. (To make the mouthpiece plug, look on page 61). Use the rest of the dowel as the slide.

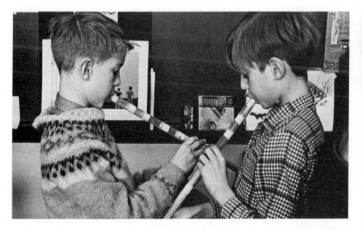

## Straw reeds

Straw reeds are easy instruments to make. All you need is a drinking straw or two and a pair of scissors.

Take a plastic or paper drinking straw (plastic works better), and flatten a section about ¾ inch long at one end. With a reasonably sharp pair of scissors, cut the two sides of the flattened portion. The end of the cut straw looks like this:

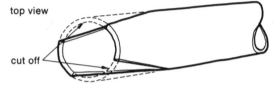

From the side, the cut straw will look a little like the open mouth of an alligator.

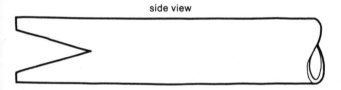

To play the straw reed, put the end of the straw into your mouth, press the straw between your teeth at a point a little beyond the end of the cut, and blow!

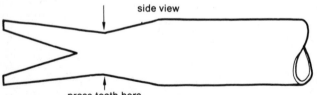

You should get a buzzing sound from the straw reed. If you don't get a sound at first, you can vary the pressure of your teeth and the position of your teeth on the straw. Eventually, you will make a sound. When you have made the sound once, it will be much easier for you to do it again.

Try cutting off bits from the end of the straw while you blow, and listen to what happens.

Or

make a slide from a longer or shorter straw to change the length of the tube and its pitch.

Or

combine short straw reeds with longer pieces of tubing to make much longer horns and pipes.

# Panpipe

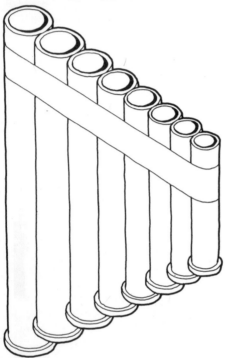

The panpipe, a very ancient instrument, has traditionally been made from reeds or bamboo. Here is a twentieth-century version.

## Materials

stiff plastic tubes from ⅜ to 1 in in diameter[1] (The set of pipes below takes about 5 feet of ⅝ inch diameter tubing)[1]

caps which fit snugly in the tubes[1] (one for each tube), or some other tight plug

masking tape

[1] For suppliers, see page 16.

## Tools

sharp scissors or utility knife

ruler

If you blow across the open end of a plastic tube which is closed at the other end, you get a clear sound of a definite pitch. The longer the tube, the lower the sound; the shorter, the higher.

Make a set of pipes from random lengths of tubing. Or, if you prefer, cut a set which plays a G major scale, by using the following dimensions (for plastic tubing ⅝ inch in diameter).

| Do | 8 in | Sol | 5 in |
| Re | 7½ in | La | 4¾ in |
| Mi | 6½ in | Ti | 4¼ in |
| Fa | 6 in | Do | 4 in |

You may need to make some fine adjustments in length to tune the pipes exactly, so cut the tubes on the generous side to allow extra for trimming if you need it. Taping the pipes together with the open ends on the same level makes them easy to play.

## Other possibilities

Many kinds of stiff, thin tubing can be used for panpipes. Also, pop bottles or test tubes filled with water to different levels can be tuned to play different notes.

# Sand Blocks

**Materials**

2 small blocks of pine or other soft wood about 1 in by 4 in by 5 in (the exact size is not important)

sandpaper or emery paper

drawing pins

cotton reels and glue, or knobs and screws

Cover one surface of each block with sandpaper, bring it up over the sides, and fasten it on with drawing pins.

**For handles,** glue an old cotton reel to the plain side of each block, or buy knobs at a hardware store and attach them with screws.

**Note:** Different grades of sandpaper and emery paper will make different sounds. You can test the sound by rubbing two bits of the paper together before you tack it to the wood. Make more than one kind of block for a variety of sounds!

# Wood-Block
# Tambourine

**Materials**

6 in block of wood, about ⅞ in by 1 ⅞
in (called 1 in by 2 in at timberyards)
crown bottle tops
nails with wide heads

**Tools**

hammer

sandpaper (to smooth rough edges)

This tambourine is made of
hardboard covered with
carpet scraps.

Remove the cork from the bottle tops. Hammer a nail through
the bottle tops partway into the wood block.

Make sure that the hole in the bottle cap is wide enough for the
cap to slide freely along the nail.

Use as many nails and as many tops on each nail as you like.

Shake the tambourine or slap the wooden side against your hand
or your knee to play it.

# Rhythm Sticks

**Materials**

pieces of doweling

**Tools**

saw

sandpaper (to smooth rough edges)

Dowels make good rhythm sticks when hit together. Thin dowels make a different sound from thicker ones. Short dowels don't sound the same as long ones.

Make pairs of rhythm sticks in different widths and lengths for a variety of sounds — 8 inches to 10 inches is a good average length.

Decorate the sticks, if you wish, with paint or varnish.

**Other possibilities**

wooden spoons

pieces of bamboo

sticks cut from broom handles

stiff plastic tubing

dried and smoothed rib-bones (the kind that are left over after you've eaten spare ribs)

# Wooden Drums

## Materials

2 pieces of thin board about ½ in thick or less (Scotch pine is a good sort or try using a large wooden cigar box)

wooden boards, about ¾ in thick (ask for 1 in stock in the width and length you need for the sides of your box)

nails

## Tools

saw

keyhole saw

Evo-stik resin

hammer

drill and ¼ in bit

Make a box with pieces of thin wood for the top and bottom, and ½ to ¾ inch wide boards for the sides. (Some people have made box drums without bottoms which have good tone.) Then cut a fairly large H-shape into the top of the box with the keyhole saw. (Drill a hole or two in the top first for inserting the saw point.) The boxes in the photograph will give you an idea of how large an H to cut in your box.

Cut the crossbar of the H **off-centre** to make two **unequal-length** flaps of wood for different tones.

The rubber end of a pencil makes a good drumstick for hitting the flaps.

Insert drawing pins or tacks, or hammer nails partway into the bottom of the box in each corner. This raises the box off the table surface and allows it to make a richer sound.

The large box in the photograph is 8½ inches square on the top and bottom. The sides are ¾ inch thick and 3½ inches wide.

The smaller boxes are 8 inches long and 4½ inches wide on top and bottom. The sides are ¾ inch thick and 2½ inches wide.

Above is an authentic African 'thumb piano'. Here's one version that is quite easy to make.

## Materials

6 or more tongue depressors or wooden spatulas

block of wood, about 8 in long

2 G-clamps (about 4 in size)

Arrange the tongue depressors across the edge of a table, so that each one sticks out to a different length.

Put the block of wood over the tongue depressors, and fasten it to the table with G-clamps.

Tighten the clamps until there is no rattle or buzz when the 'piano' is played.

To change the sounds, loosen the clamps and alter the overhanging lengths.

**Variations**

You can make portable finger pianos, too.

**Materials**
thin pieces of wood
plastic flower pot, tin or other hollow container
Èvo-stik resin W
5 tongue depressors or wooden spatulas
7 or 8 ice-lolly sticks

**Tools**
single-edge razor blade or stanley knife
sandpaper

The 'piano' on the right in the picture is made of thin strips of wood glued onto other strips. These are then glued together and glued onto a piece of plank as a base.

The one on the left uses an upside-down cardboard bucket, with a little hole cut in it, as a resonator and support. Cut one of the tongue depressors to fit across the bucket, just touching the inside rim. You can cut it with a knife or razor blade or score it top and bottom so that it will break off clean. Use this tongue depressor to mark the other four for cutting. Then line up five ice-lolly sticks so that they stick out different amounts, and cut off the other ends evenly.

Now make a sandwich with three of the cut tongue depressors glued together, then the cut ends of the ice-lolly sticks glued in at right angles, then the other two tongue depressors. Glue two halves of ice-lolly stick on top of each other and under the finger edge of the piano to prop it up. Glue the piano in place against the rim of the bucket, tape it to the sides to hold it firm, and let it dry overnight before you play it.

To make a 'piano' like the one in this picture, glue three pieces of wood together with one sticking out between the other two. Then cut strips in the middle board to make the keys. The thin dowel between the two back pieces gives the instrument a richer tone.

You can tune all the finger pianos by trimming the wooden strips with a little hacksaw blade 'minisaw'. One end of the hacksaw blade is covered with tape wrapped around two ice-lolly sticks for a handle. This tool costs very little to make and is good for all sorts of small-size sawing and whittling jobs.

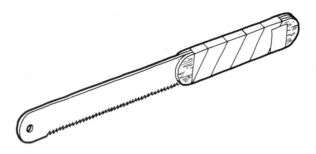

# Rattles

Any container that can be sealed and easily shaken, and any material that will move freely inside the container can be used.

Both the container (its size, shape and the material from which it is made) and what is inside it will influence the sound that the rattle will make. Try the same contents in several different containers and, also, different contents in the same kind of container, to find the most appealing sound combination.

Since there are so many possibilities, try several combinations and make rattles for different tonal and rhythmic effects.

## Containers

paper cups (those with lids which are easy to close securely)

plastic detergent or bleach bottles

individual-serving cereal boxes

small plastic boxes or tins

match boxes

cough-sweet tins or sticking-plaster tins

plastic pots with lids (e.g. cottage cheese or large yoghurt pots)

small screw-top jars

## Contents

any sort of dried beans, peas or seeds

rice

table salt or sugar

marbles

feathers

sand

gravel

# Telephones

Here are some devices that convey sounds over long distances.

### String telephones

Thread each end of a long piece of string through a hole made in the bottom of a paper cup or tin can. Talk into one cup and listen through the other.

Plastic-coated paper coffee cups work very well. Tie paper clips to the string ends to keep them from slipping back through the cups. Pull the string tight.

You can make a party line by tying other cups and strings into the main line.

## Talking tubes

To make a talking tube, attach funnels to both ends of any piece
of hose — a garden hose, the hose from a vacuum cleaner or
portable hair dryer.

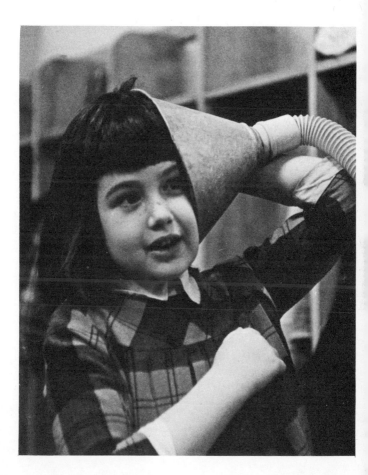

# e✕tensions

**Extensions** is an entirely new concept in schools publishing. It recognizes no subject barriers. It has no rigid series approach. It attempts to close the gap between the textbook and the 'real' book.

**Extensions** will surely find a warm welcome in many classrooms. It is likely to be welcomed in as many homes. Attractively and lavishly illustrated, they are all published in convenient paperback format.

Handbooks and sourcebooks predominate — books which involve children in learning by activity. But all these titles are (we believe) books that will work by interesting, arousing and involving.

**Rights**
A Handbook for People under Age
Nan Berger

What is a right? When does a need or a demand become a right?
What do you do if your rights are being ignored?

Starting from these questions, this book looks at the rights of
young people. It aims not only to investigate general issues, but
also to provide concrete advice for anyone under age. **Rights** is a
unique combination of discussion book and handbook.

**Curious Naturalists**
Revised Edition
Niko Tinbergen

As a young man, just out of university, Niko Tinbergen walked along some sand dunes in his native Holland. His attention was suddenly caught by the behaviour of some sand wasps . . .

Niko Tinbergen went on to become a world-famous scientist, winner of a Nobel Prize and one of the foremost authorities on animal behaviour. **Curious Naturalists** is a special kind of autobiography. It tells the story of his work but it is also a fascinating insight into what it is like to be a creative scientist.

**The Pollution Handbook**
The ACE/Sunday Times Clean Air and Water Surveys
Richard Mabey

Pollution is everybody's business. No one can escape dirty air or contaminated water. Keeping watch on the state of these things is an immense and important task.

You can help. **The Pollution Handbook,** based on the highly successful children's surveys of air and water pollution organized by the Advisory Centre of Education, explains just what pollution is, how you can keep an expert eye on it in your neighbourhood, and what steps you can take to reduce it.

**A Touch on the Times**
**Songs of Social Change 1790 to 1914**
Edited by Roy Palmer

Before the days of national newspapers and television you could often find the ballad sellers. For a penny or less you could have an account of a terrible murder, a protest at the price of meat or the story of a battle.

Roy Palmer has collected some of the best here to show the way ordinary people reacted to social change. The book is illustrated throughout with old photographs, many of them published here for the first time.

**Science Experiments You Can Eat**
Vicki Cobb

You may never have thought there was anything scientific about meringues, mayonnaise or cupcakes. But making them involves solutions, emulsions and some very complex chemical reactions.

The kitchen is actually a very well-equipped laboratory. This book shows you how you can make some very good things to eat — and learn about science at the same time.

# connexions

**A series of topic books for students in schools and colleges of further education.**

**Shelter**
Nan Fairbrother

We pass through any number of shelters in our lives — out of the womb, into the cot; parents' home, a bed-sitter, a house of our own, finally, perhaps, an old people's home. On the way many more temporary resting places: schools, clubs, offices, a hotel room for a weekend. All of these are more than bricks and mortar, and give us, if we're lucky, some sort of emotional security as well as protection from the weather.

When we first asked the late Nan Fairbrother to write this book it was to be chiefly about buildings and town planning. But Nan quickly showed us how it was impossible to consider 'shelter' in physical terms apart from people's needs as humans — for company, privacy, growth and security and all those subtle qualities that make a house into a home. The result is **Shelter**, a book which begins with an examination of these needs and only secondly looks at the way they are met by the dwelling places we create for ourselves. The story is vividly brought to life by first-hand case histories of particular groups of people, and the environments that they live in — gypsies, old people, young families in high-rise flats, the physically handicapped.

Nan Fairbrother was perhaps our most sensitive writer on the man-made environment. Her book **New Lives, New Landscapes,** about how we might alter the look and shape of Britain to meet our changing needs, was awarded the W.H. Smith Literary Award just before her death in 1971.

**Work**
Colin Ward

Automation is spreading, unemployment is rising. Every year
there are more school-leavers in the queues outside the labour
exchanges. Does it matter, as long as there is the dole? Or do we
**need** to work to keep our self-respect, or because we are a
naturally creative species, or just to stop ourselves being literally
bored to death?

Colin Ward quotes a sociologist who found that 'quite often the
worker comes to work on Monday worn out from his weekend
activities, especially "do-it-yourself"'. **Work** is about this
paradoxical situation. The question it asks above all is — what do
we want out of work? A fair wage or satisfaction as well? Do many
of the methods employers use to try and make labour less tedious
— like automation — actually create **more** problems? Will we ever
be free of strikes and bad workmanship and the almost universal
notion that work is a chore, until each worker feels he is as much
his own man as he does on those do-it-yourself weekends?

Colin Ward will be no stranger to **Connexions** readers. He is the
author of a previous volume on **Violence**. He is currently
education officer of the Town and Country Planning Association,
editor of that lively monthly magazine for schools, BEE (the
**Bulletin of Environmental Education**) and is very much involved
in the development of new social-studies courses.

**The Lawbreakers**
Ray Jenkins

During the last twelve months most of us have committed at least one crime: 'borrowed' paper from school or college, trespassed, ignored the speed limit. But very few of us were caught and even fewer convicted.

In addition, the numbers of those convicted are rising all the time. Do people no longer think that law is important, or is it simply that the pressures which have always produced crime are increasing?

**The Lawbreakers** looks at the nature of law, why we need it and why we break it, who administers it, and how those that break it are punished. It asks us to remember that the law is not perfect: it can make mistakes, and must change to meet the needs of a changing society.

This revised edition brings **The Lawbreakers** up to date by dealing with the changes brought about by recent legislation concerning young people and the law.

Ray Jenkins learnt a great deal about the workings of the law during a spell as a 'Z Cars' scriptwriter. Since then he has written many scripts for TV, radio, film and stage, including schools' series like 'Listening and Writing' and 'Acting Shakespeare'. Before he became a professional author, Ray Jenkins taught for three and a half years in a London comprehensive school. He is married with two children.

**Break for Commercials**
**An Examination of Advertising Techniques**
Edith Rudinger and Vic Kelly

**Break for Commercials** takes a cool look at advertisements, at the function they perform in our society, and at the devices they use in trying to persuade us to buy.

Advertising has always been a source of argument. Ever since men began selling to each other, it's been accused of exaggeration and deception, of encouraging people to want goods they don't need. Now more serious charges are being laid against it: that, for instance, it encourages snobbishness and materialism, and equates ideas like mother-love with nothing more than providing plenty of breakfast food.

But are these criticisms fair? We all enjoy some adverts, even if (we think) they don't necessarily affect our buying habits. And we know that it would be impossible for society to survive unless manufacturers give prospective buyers some information about their goods.

**Break for Commercials** encourages us to sort out the helpful advertising from the harmful, and to try and understand just what the advertisers are really up to.

Edith Rudinger is Head of Publications at the Consumers' Association, and Vic Kelly is Head of the Secondary Department at Goldsmiths' College, London. They have worked together before, on the book **Which? in Secondary Schools: Maths and science.**

**Food**
**The Impact of Food Technology on Everyday Life**
Richard Mabey

There is a saying that 'You are what you eat'. It's also true that you are **how** you eat. In all parts of the world eating is much more than a way of simply keeping alive. The production and preparation of food occupy vast amounts of time and energy, not just in industry but also in the home. Meals bring families together and eating them provides one of our most enjoyable leisure experiences.

**Food** is about this close involvement of food with our social lives, and in particular about the way our old-established eating habits are being affected by new ways of providing food. For even in this most basic area of life, technology has moved in. The growing demand for 'convenience' foods, for food which is plentiful, cheap and easy to prepare, is making far-reaching changes: farming, and therefore the countryside, is being run more and more as an industry; synthetic foods are being developed and synthetic chemicals added to natural ones; and quite new sorts of food shops and restaurants are springing up. **Food** asks how all this is affecting our private family and social lives, and, in conclusion, what may be the impact of Western food technology on those hungry countries of the world that we are trying to help feed.

Richard Mabey is general editor of Connexions (he wrote the first volume, **Behind the Scene**) and also a freelance writer, specializing in educational, environmental and natural history topics. He has lectured in social studies at a college of further education, and has written a book on the edible wild plants of Britain.